EYE ILLUSIONS ™

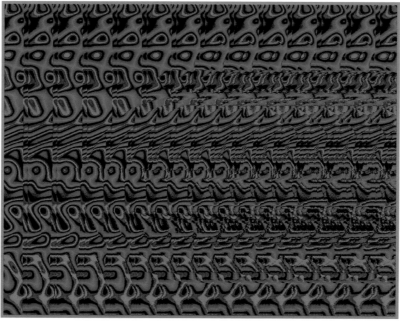

Written by Jim Anderson
Book Design by TXF Graphics

Modern Publishing
A Division of Unisystems, Inc.
New York, New York 10022
Printed in the U.S.A.

INTRODUCTION

Welcome to a new world! Hidden within the beautiful abstract pictures in this book are exciting three-dimensional images. All you need to do is look at the pictures in a special way, relax, and the images will unfold in front of you as if by magic. You will see images of animals and toys, people and things — all in brilliant color and sharp detail. You might even be tempted to reach out and touch them.

The wonderful images in this book are called "stereograms." They are flat, two-dimensional pictures that, when viewed in the right way, appear to have three dimensions. Early 3-D pictures were really two images, and you needed special glasses or a special viewer to look at them. Thanks to modern computer technology, stereograms are now single images that can be viewed directly by anyone!

For hundreds of years, scientists have been studying how vision works. Artists began using this knowledge to draw 3-D pictures over 150 years ago, but since they drew by hand, it took them a long time to create even one image. The development of computers changed everything. Starting in the 1960s, artists used computer graphics to create ever more complex and beautiful 3-D art. At first, the 3-D images were simple shapes and designs. As computer graphic technology improved, and as the artists grew in their craft, more detailed and exciting pictures were created.

We can see these pictures in three dimensions because all human beings have "binocular" vision. Our eyes are several inches apart, so each eye sees things from a slightly different angle. This information is combined in the brain to give us a 3-D view of the world. Things not only have height and width, they have depth as well. Stereograms, though they look like simple abstract patterns, actually contain all the information the brain needs to "see" a 3-D image. The information for the right eye is on the right side of the picture, and that for the left eye is on the left side. By relaxing the focus of our eyes, we allow the two sides to overlap, and the brain is "tricked" into seeing a 3-D picture. It's a simple idea made possible thanks to complex technology. Truly, these 3-D pictures show us a new world!

INSTRUCTIONS

To see these 3-D images, you need the right setting. First, find a quiet place with bright lighting, and make sure the picture you look at is evenly lit. Then sit up straight, take a deep breath, and relax. This is very important. The more relaxed you are, the easier it will be to find the images, and the more fun you will have. Also, be patient, especially in the beginning. It may take several minutes before you can see the picture in three dimensions. So take it easy and don't give up.

There are several ways of viewing the 3-D images in this book:

Method One
Begin by looking at the cover picture. The cover is shiny, and you should be able to see your reflection, or the reflection of a light in it. Look at the picture on the cover, but focus your eyes on the reflection. This will make your eyes relax and go out of focus. Stare at the picture for a minute or two until you "feel" something start to happen. Just relax, continue staring, and the 3-D image will appear.

Method Two
Another way to see the 3-D image is to bring the picture right up to your nose. Don't try to see the image — just let your eyes go completely out of

focus. Then, while keeping your eyes out of focus, move the picture back to about arm's length. Keep looking at it with your eyes relaxed, and after a little while, the 3-D image will "pop" out.

Method Three

A third approach is to try and "see through" the picture. Look at the page, relax your eyes, and imagine you are looking "beyond" the book. Keep looking for a few minutes. Remember, patience is important. So is relaxation. Just take it easy and enjoy yourself. In time, a beautiful 3-D image will appear to you.

These three methods make up the "parallel-viewing" technique. There is also a "cross-eyed" technique that is more comfortable for some people.

Method Four

To view the images in the cross-eyed way, bring your finger, or a pen or pencil, up close to your eyes. Focus on the finger, pen or pencil. As you hold this focus, look at the stereogram. It may take a few minutes, but the 3-D image will appear. Once you develop one technique, try to develop the other. Sometimes, different techniques allow you to see slightly different images in the same stereogram. For example, if you look at a 3-D image of birds flying in the sky, the parallel-viewing technique may show you the birds in front, with the clouds in the background. With the cross-eyed technique, however, you may see the clouds in front, looking as if the birds have already flown through them leaving bird-shaped holes!

There are 14 images in this book, each with a riddle to help you discover what it is. If you're patient and keep at it, you will soon be able to see all of them. Then you truly will be an expert in the world of 3-D!

Opposite: *How do you cross a river or a lake without getting wet? Use this! The American Indians used it, and so did the early settlers. It's fun to use on summer vacation, too. You can make it out of tree bark or wood or metal. If it gets wet, just turn it upside down to dry!*

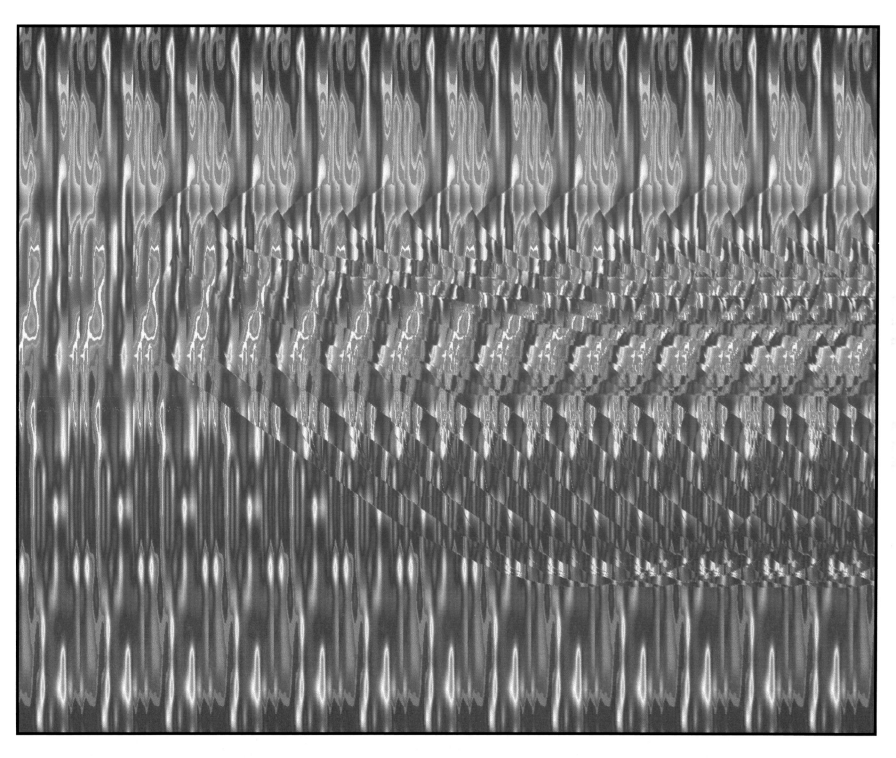

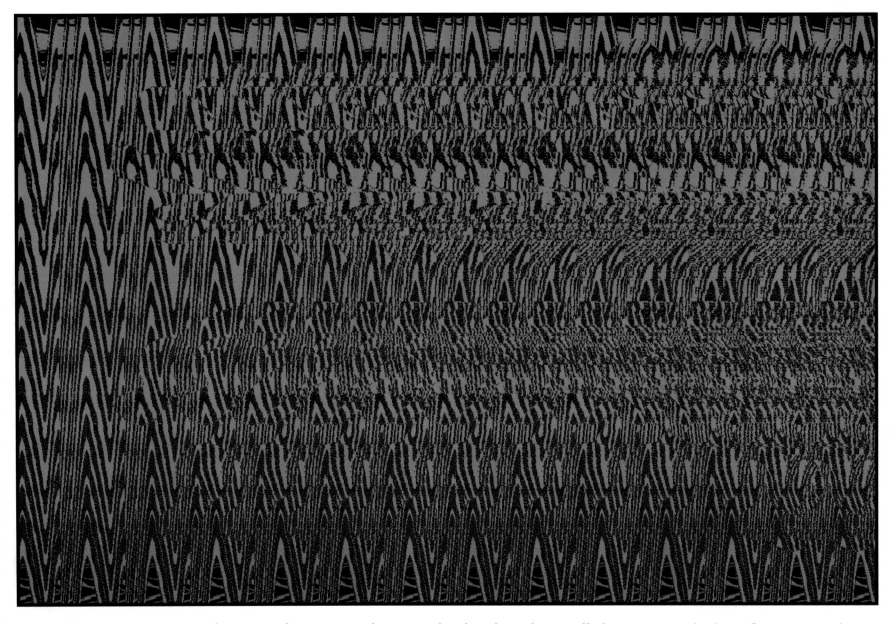

This is a nice pet, but you have to take it to the barbershop all the time! It helps if you speak French, too. It's got four feet and a tail, and loves to play. Throw a ball and watch it have fun. Then give it some food — it loves to eat!

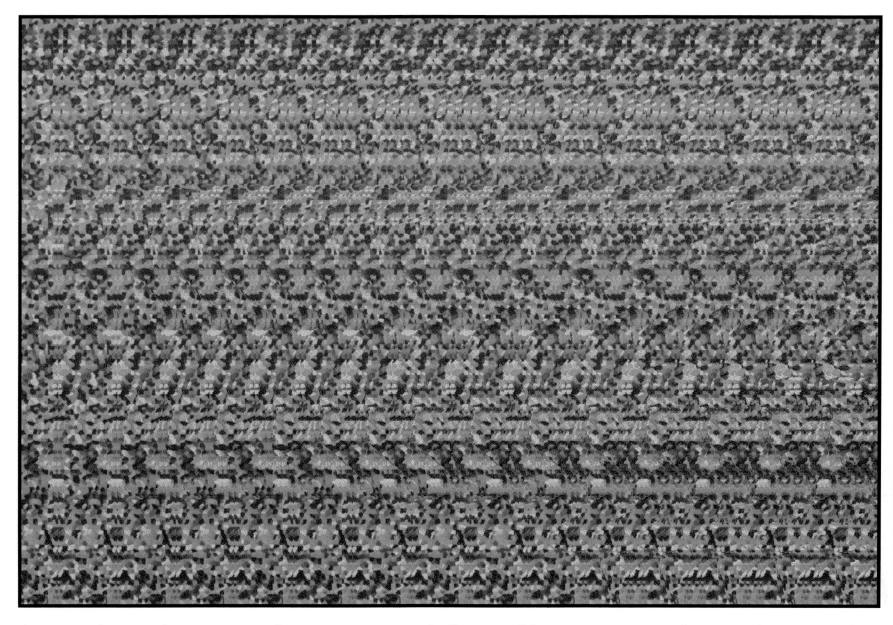

We live underwater, so if you want to say hello, you'll have to put on a face mask! We're not fish, but "fish" is in our name. We can't be seen in the sky, but we look like something that can. Next time you go swimming in the ocean, come close and we'll wave at you!

Up, up, and away! This will take you into the clouds, but it's not an airplane. In fact, it doesn't even have wings! But it floats in the air like a bubble and doesn't make a sound. Climb in with your friends, relax, and take a bird's-eye view of things.

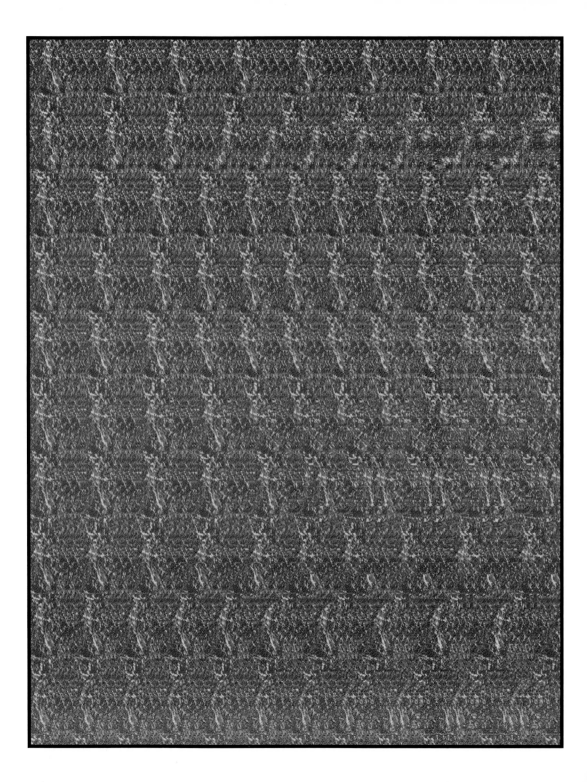

Is he funny or is he scary? Sometimes he's both. You won't see him on the street, but he's the star of the circus. He's tall and short, fat and skinny, and he always has a smile — because it's painted on!

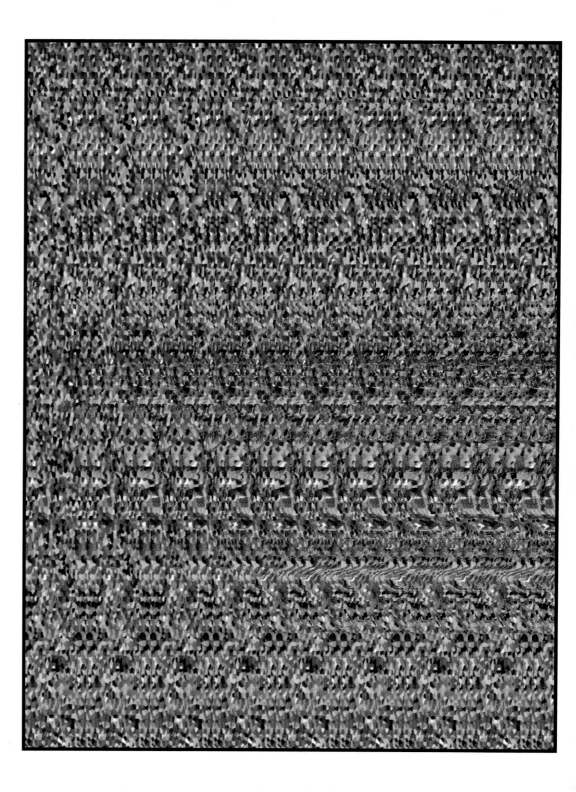

This will take you from here to there, especially when there's a river in the way. Made of metal or wood or concrete, it's built to last a long, long time. Some are so old, they're famous. Maybe you cross over one on the way to school or work, or when you visit friends.

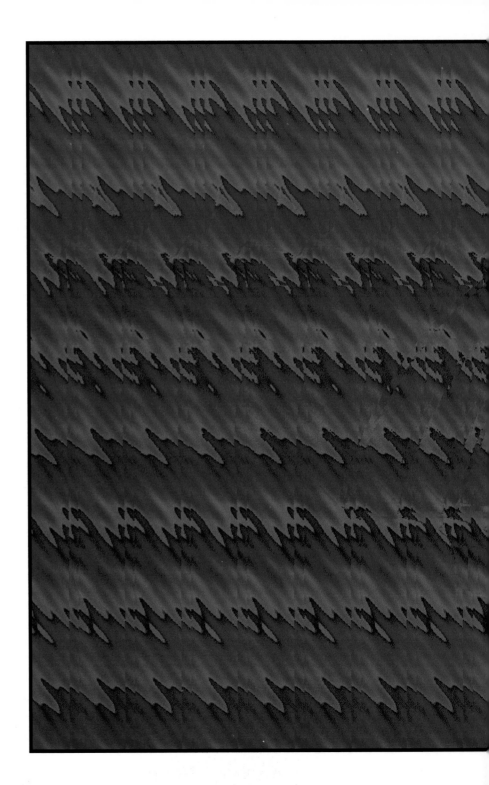

Opposite:
Once upon a time, only kings and queens lived in this. Now you can make it out of sand when you're at the beach. Trouble is, when the tide comes in, it washes away. But cheer up! You can come back the next day and make another.

Overleaf:
Do you have one of these at home? Is this how you get to work, go shopping, or visit friends? It has four wheels, but it's not a bus or a truck. If you're getting one for the first time, don't forget to step on the gas!

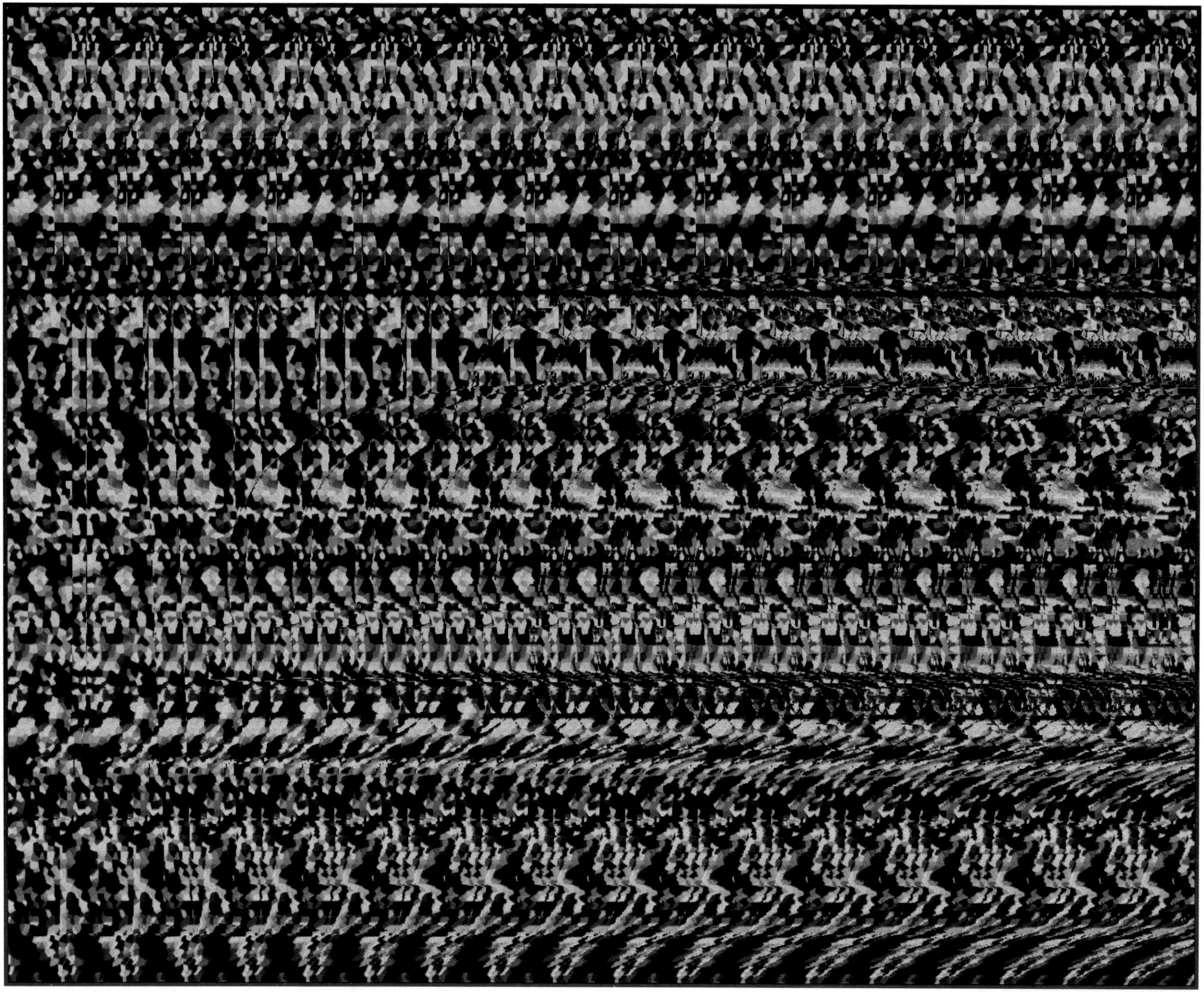

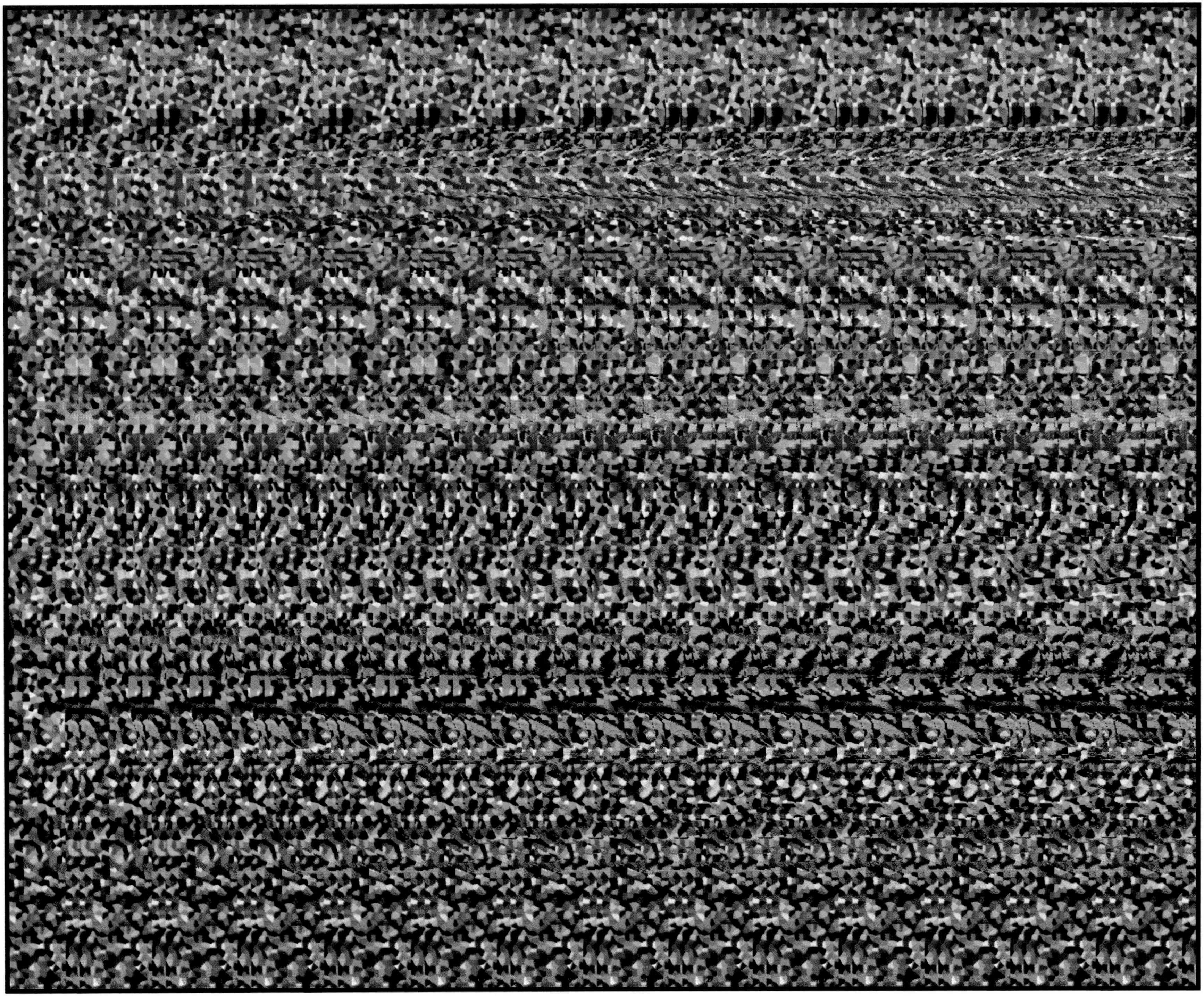

Previous page:
Dive! Dive! This is the way to travel underwater and never get wet. Sometimes sailors will spend a whole year in one of these and not once step onto dry land! Some of these are as big as a whale. Others are as small as a car. Can you see it? What is it?

Opposite:
Put on your hard hat! Get ready to get dirty! People use this to clean things up in a BIG way. Have you seen them on the street? Maybe you wish you had your own whenever you are down in the "dumps" about having to clean the house!

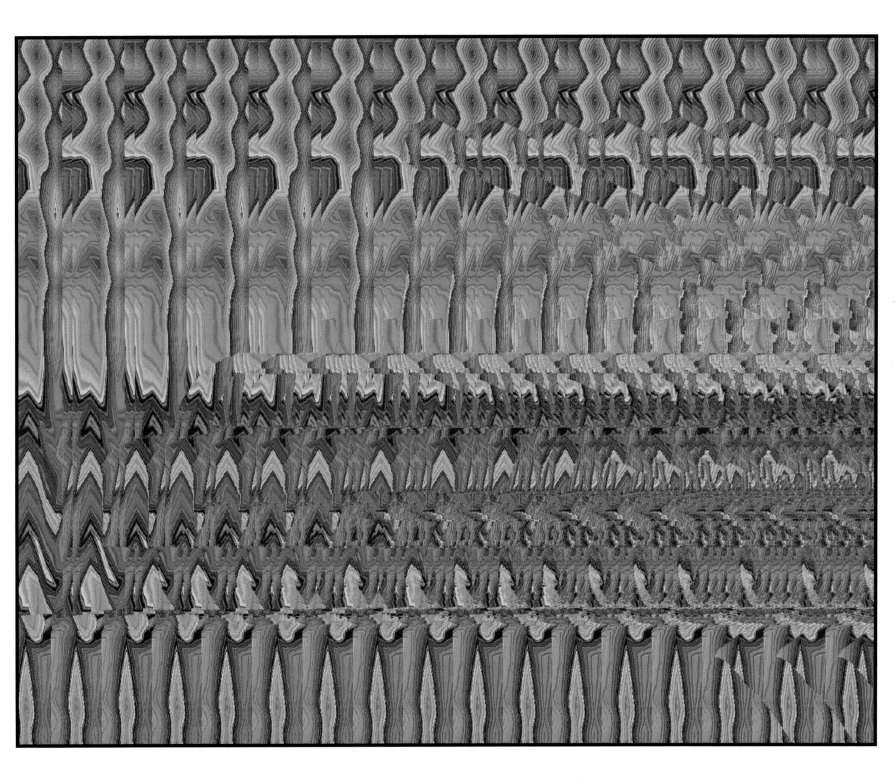

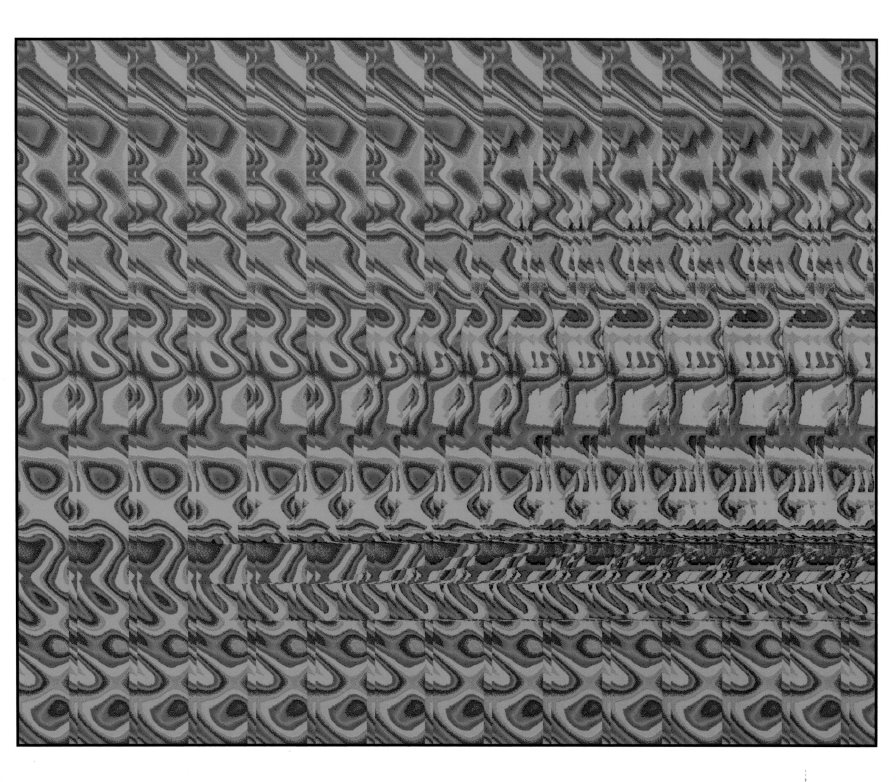

Opposite:
Anchors Aweigh! Here's the perfect mode of transportation for a breezy day. Everything will seem shipshape once you're afloat, as long as you remember one rule: Don't rock the boat!

Make no "bones" about it, this person knows how to have fun on Halloween! He — or she — just shakes and rattles and rolls the night away, then spends the daytime sleeping. What a life! But someone should buy this one dinner. Looks like he or she hasn't eaten a good meal in a long time.

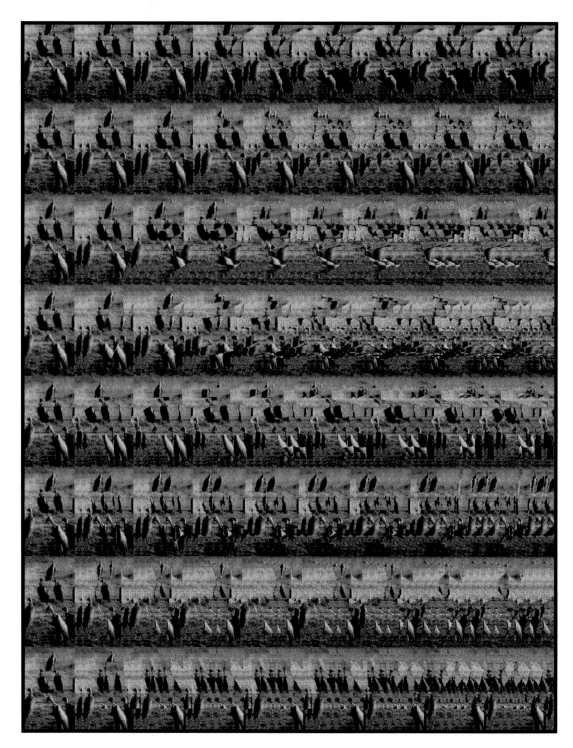

Blast off! These will take you up in the air. Some will take you into orbit around the earth. Some will even take you to the moon and back! They are big and tall, and make a really loud noise when they take off. Maybe someday, you'll ride one into outer space.

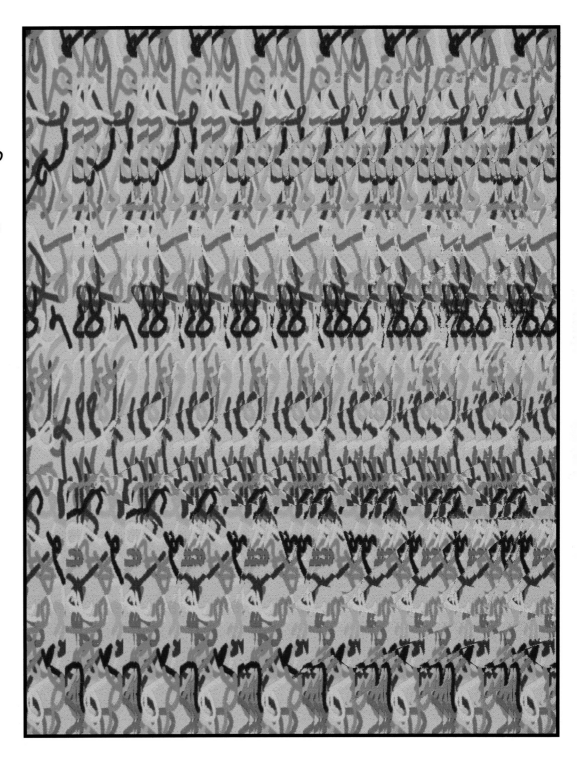

You don't want to go swimming when this is in the water! It's sleek and swift, it has sharp teeth, and it's always hungry. It travels in packs, but it's not a dog, so don't pet it. These "jaws" just love to eat, so you can look — but don't touch!

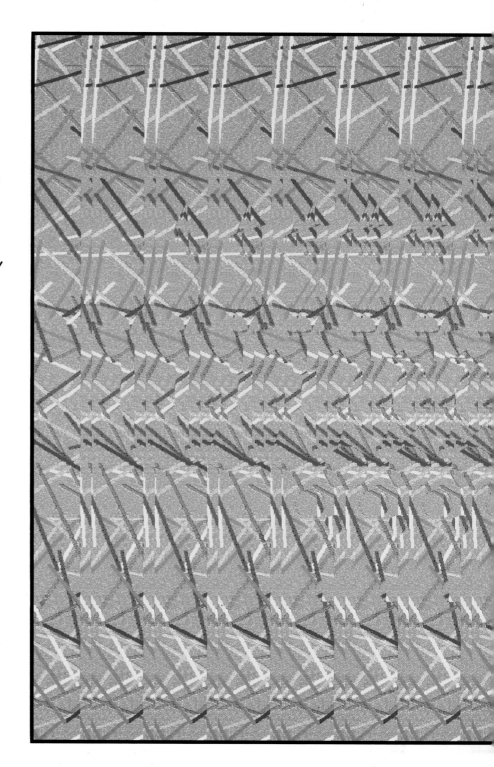

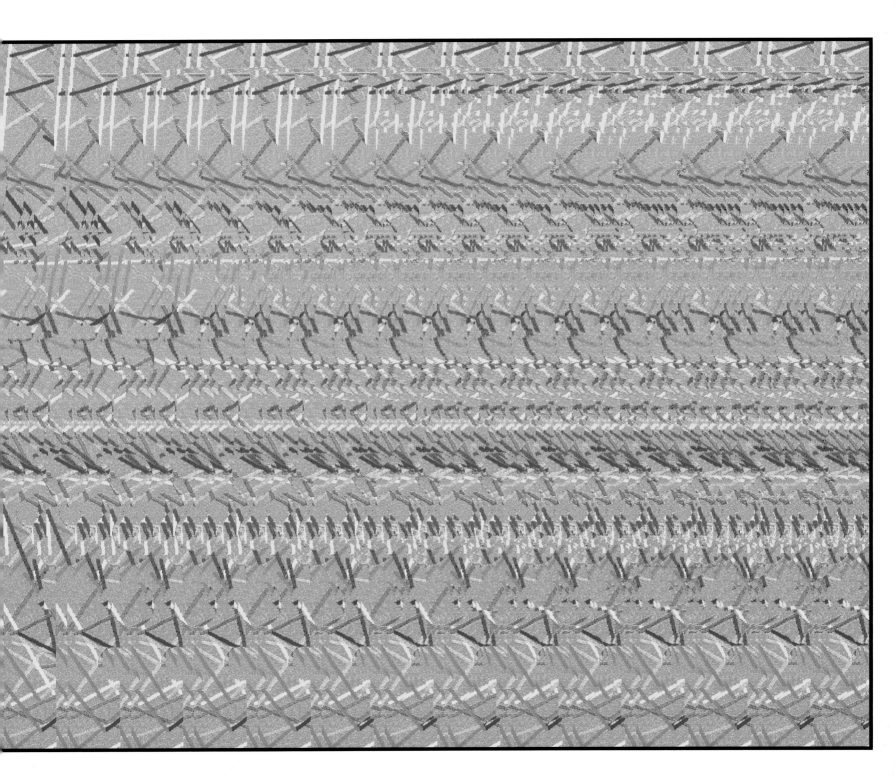

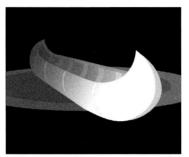

Page 5   Canoe

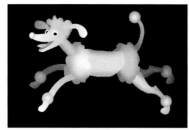

Page 6   French Poodle

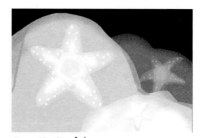

Page 7   Starfish

Page 8   Hot Air Balloon

Page 9   Clown

Pages 10-11   Bridge

Page 12   Sand Castle

Page 14   Car

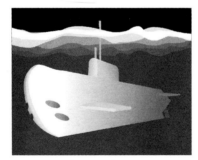

Page 15   Submarine

Page 17   Dump Truck

Page 18   Sail Boat

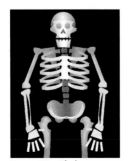

Page 20   Skeleton

Page 21   Space Rockets

Pages 22-23   Sharks